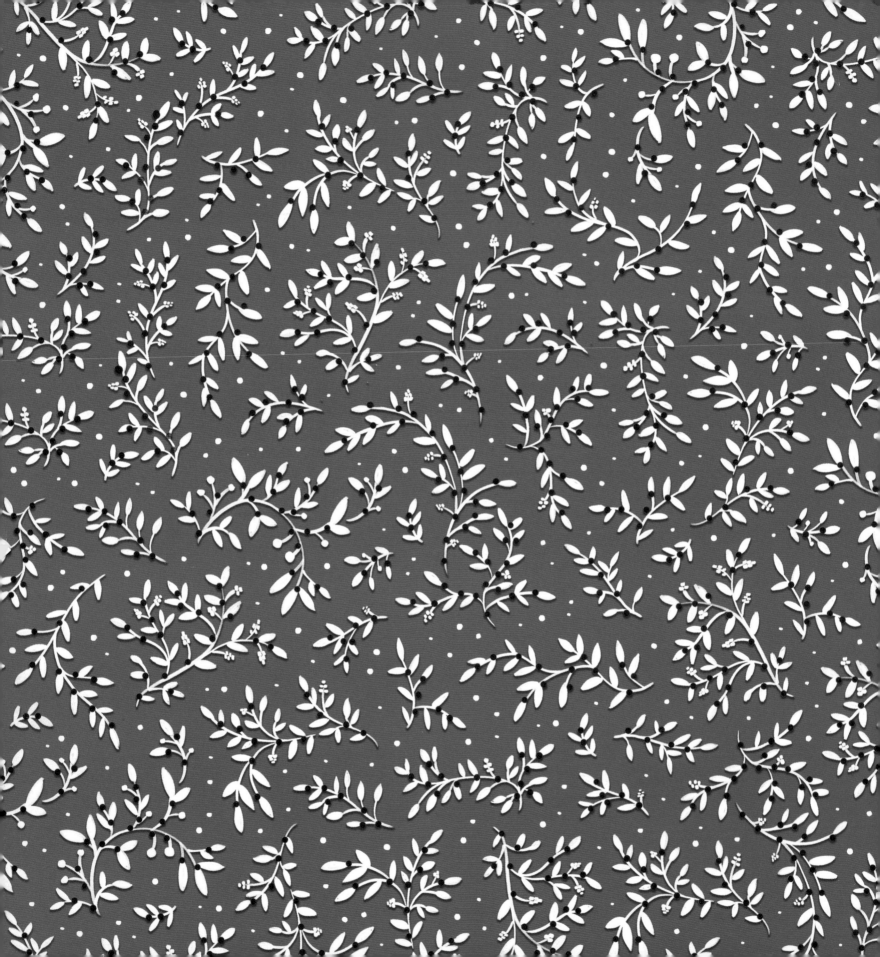

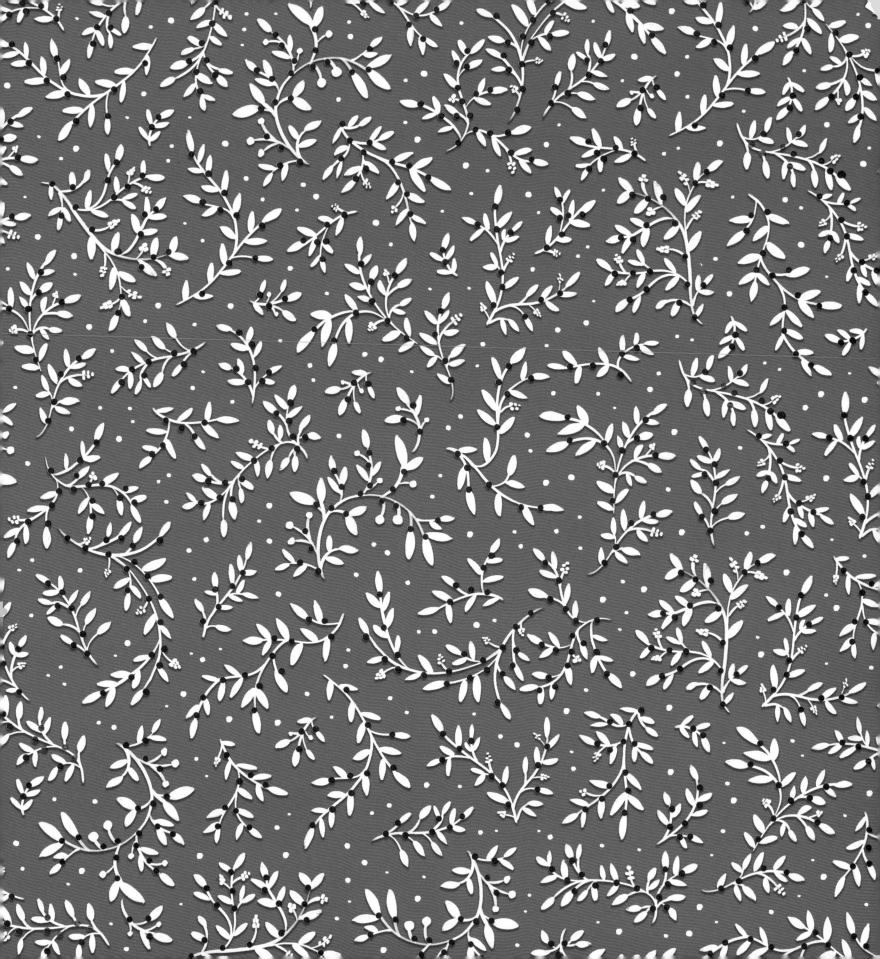

IMAGINE THAT

Licensed exclusively to Imagine That Publishing Ltd
Tide Mill Way, Woodbridge, Suffolk, IP12 1AP, UK
www.imaginethat.com
Design copyright © 2020 Imagine That Group Ltd
Illustration copyright © 2020 Andrea Petrlik/Shutterstock.com
All rights reserved
2 4 6 8 9 7 5 3 1
Manufactured in China

Written by Frederic Austin
Illustrated by Andrea Petrlik

ISBN 978-1-78958-727-2

A catalogue record for this book is available from the British Library

The TWELVE days of CHRISTMAS

Illustrations by Andrea Petrlik

1

On the **FIRST DAY** of Christmas,
my true love gave to me ...
A PARTRIDGE IN A PEAR TREE.

On the **SECOND DAY** of Christmas,
my true love gave to me ...
TWO TURTLE DOVES,

And a partridge in a pear tree.

3

On the **THIRD DAY** of Christmas,
my true love gave to me ...
THREE FRENCH HENS,

Two turtle doves,
And a partridge in a pear tree.

On the **FOURTH DAY** of Christmas,
my true love gave to me ...
FOUR CALLING BIRDS,

Three French hens,
Two turtle doves,
And a partridge in a pear tree.

On the **FIFTH DAY** of Christmas,
my true love gave to me ...
FIVE GOLDEN RINGS,

Four calling birds,
Three French hens,
Two turtle doves,
And a partridge in a pear tree.

6

On the **SIXTH DAY** of Christmas,
my true love gave to me ...
SIX GEESE A-LAYING,

Five golden rings,

Four calling birds,

Three French hens,

Two turtle doves,

And a partridge in a pear tree.

On the SEVENTH DAY of Christmas,
my true love gave to me ...
SEVEN SWANS A-SWIMMING,

Six geese a-laying,

Five golden rings,

Four calling birds,

Three French hens,

Two turtle doves,

And a partridge in a pear tree.

8

On the **EIGHTH DAY** of Christmas,
my true love gave to me ...
EIGHT MAIDS A-MILKING,

Seven swans a-swimming,

Six geese a-laying,

Five golden rings,

Four calling birds,

Three French hens,

Two turtle doves,

And a partridge in a pear tree.

On the **NINTH DAY** of Christmas,
my true love gave to me ...
NINE LADIES DANCING,

Eight maids a-milking,

Seven swans a-swimming,

Six geese a-laying,

Five golden rings,

Four calling birds,

Three French hens,

Two turtle doves,

And a partridge in a pear tree.

10

On the **TENTH DAY** of Christmas,
my true love gave to me ...
TEN LORDS A-LEAPING,

Nine ladies dancing,

Eight maids a-milking,

Seven swans a-swimming,

Six geese a-laying,

Five golden rings,

Four calling birds,

Three French hens,

Two turtle doves,

And a partridge in a pear tree.

11

On the **ELEVENTH DAY** of Christmas,
my true love gave to me ...
ELEVEN PIPERS PIPING,

Ten lords a-leaping,
Nine ladies dancing,
Eight maids a-milking,
Seven swans a-swimming,
Six geese a-laying,
Five golden rings,
Four calling birds,
Three French hens,
Two turtle doves,
And a partridge in a pear tree.

12

On the **TWELFTH DAY** of Christmas,
my true love gave to me ...
TWELVE DRUMMERS DRUMMING,

Eleven pipers piping,
Ten lords a-leaping,
Nine ladies dancing,
Eight maids a-milking,
Seven swans a-swimming,
Six geese a-laying,
Five golden rings,
Four calling birds,
Three French hens,
Two turtle doves,
And a partridge in a pear tree.

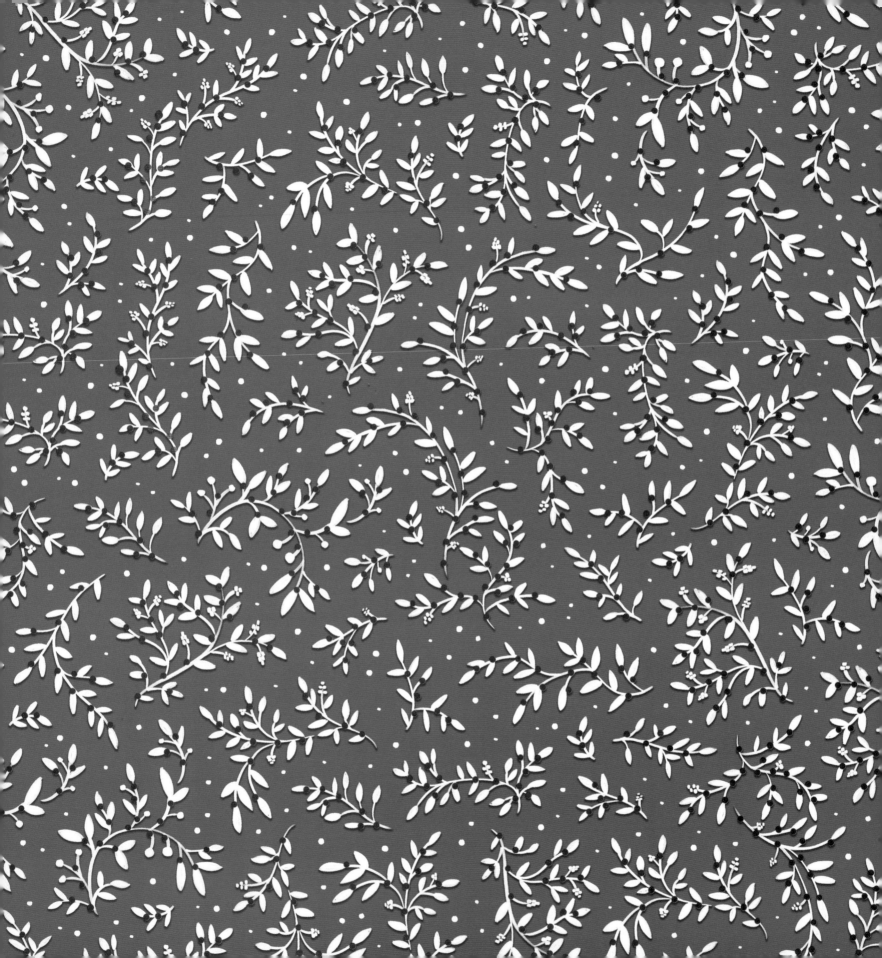

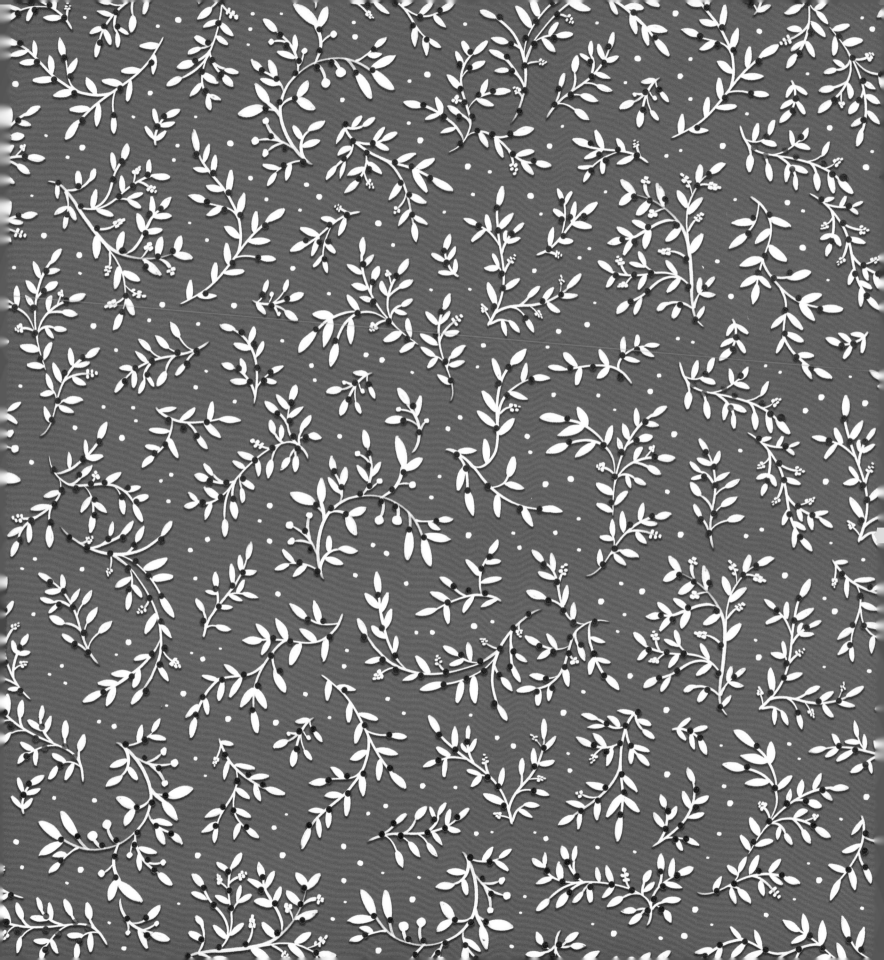